The Elijah Project for Teens
by Andrea M. Polnaszek, LCSW

The Elijah Project for Teens

© 2014 by Andrea M. Polnaszek, LCSW

Cover artwork created by Matthew Reddy
Additional illustrations by Matthew Reddy, Christina Rambo and Izzy Polnaszek
Page layout design created by Lisa Fischer
Assistant to the author: Renee Wurzer

Printed in the United States of America
ISBN: 978-1-7329824-7-5

Dedication

I want to dedicate the workbook to the Fellowship Church Youth Group who walked through Elijah's journey with me. They honestly processed and shared their fears and joys together.

And to my son Will who has patiently grown up with his Mom practicing counseling skills on him.

Contents

The Elijah Project for Teens

Introduction

This whole thing got started when God helped me remember all that He had provided for me while I was going through a time of fear, anger and hopelessness. God used the story of Elijah from 3,000 years ago to remind me that He was protecting and providing for me today. I wrote a workbook for adults to share my story and offer a way for adults to process their stories. After writing the workbook, I spoke to a large gathering of women and shared my story and Elijah's story. This talk led to a book that went into more detail than the workbook linking my story with Elijah's journey.

I thought it would be fun to adapt The Elijah Project adult class for my youth group. The Elijah Project for Teens is the result of the adaptation. It doesn't matter how old you are, we all need to remember that God is protecting and providing for us today.

We hope you find the activities helpful.

Andrea

Some Helpful Things to Know

This book is based on a strengths perspective, drawing on the truth of the Bible that says God is enough. He is all we need.

When you see:

Stop. Take a minute to think of a way that God has protected or provided for you today. Then turn your thankfulness into a prayer. This workbook is based on Elijah's journey with God. After each section of the story we will look to see where God protected and provided for Elijah and where He is protecting and providing for you.

God's protection: God has His eye on you even when bad things are happening in this broken world.

God's provision: God knows what we really need and sometimes it looks different from what we think we need or want.

1   I believe it is very important to identify and understand what you feel. I believe that God gave you feelings so that you could enjoy your life with God. Through out the workbook we will practice identifying how we feel. There are four main groups of feelings: Scared, Mad, Sad and Joy. Often times we feel one emotion on the surface, like for instance someone says something mean to you and you instantly become angry. This is our "fight" emotion. When we spend time understanding why we felt anger we may discover that rather than feeling angry we were really afraid. The more we dig into our feelings and understand them, the less we will act out of emotion and the more we will express the heart of what is going on.

2   I believe that Satan is alive in our broken world and his primary aim is to "rob, kill, steal and destroy." He is looking to disconnect us from God and each other. When we feel alone... bad things end up happening. We make uninformed decisions and often feel extremely sad. I believe that God's protection and provision is waiting for us if we seek God first.

3   I believe in the power of prayer. I believe that God wants us to talk to him about everything. He wants to know our good and bad feelings. He wants to know about our good and bad experiences. He wants to know everything.

Before We Begin

Activity 1:

Take a few moments to look at the feeling dolls below. Identify one word in each feeling category to describe how you are feeling today. Refer back to this page throughout your journey to find words to describe how you feel.

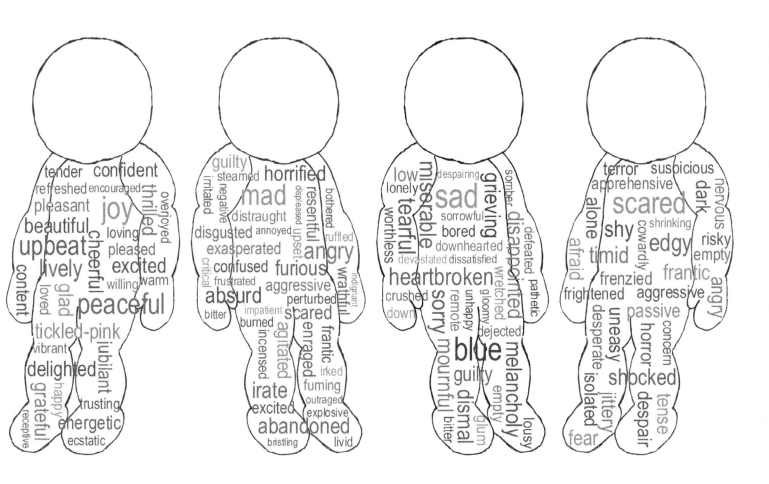

Who was Elijah?

Elijah was from Tishbe in the land of Gilead. He said to Ahab, "I serve the Lord. He is the God of Israel. You can be sure that he lives. And you can be just as sure that there won't be any dew or rain on the whole land. There won't be any during the next few years. It won't come until I say so." – *1 Kings 17:1*

Elijah was a man from Tishbe. He was a herdsman, working the land like a farmer. He learned the ways of the God of Abraham, Isaac and Jacob. Elijah had a special calling on his life. He was a prophet which meant that God spoke to him and gave him messages to tell the people. Even his name meant: "Yahweh is God."

Activity 2: Timeline

Have you ever felt insignificant: being from a small town doing an ordinary job? Elijah would "get that." Tishbe was a small town and he probably grew up working the land.

Write down every that you can remember - big and small - on the timeline below.

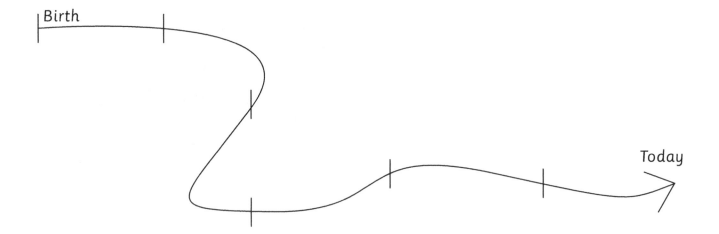

Activity 3: Who am I?

➡ Scan your body head to toe. How do you feel today?

➡ Where do you feel good, happy, or relaxed?

➡ Where do you feel bad, angry, or stressed?

➡ Use colors, words, and pictures to share how you feel.

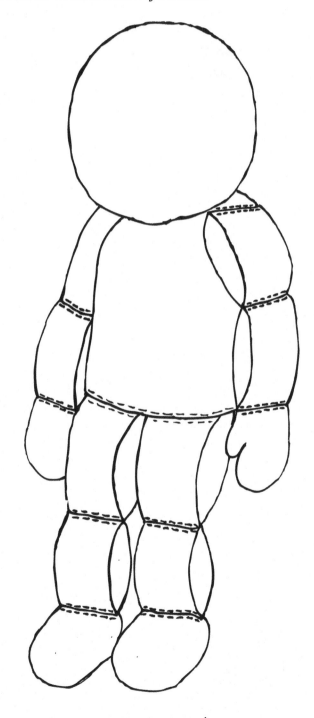

Tell Your Story

Like Elijah you have a story too. Your life experience is valuable. Start with when you were born and try to remember the most important things that have happened so far in your life. Feel free to refer back to page 6 timeline.

Activity 4:

➡ Use the comic strip form to tell the story of your life.

#1

#2

#3

#4

#5

#6

#7

#8

The Brook Dries Up

"Then a message from the Lord came to Elijah. It said, "Leave this place. Go east and hide in the Kerwith Valley. It is east of the Jordan River. You will drink water from the brook. I have ordered some ravens to feed you there."

So Elijah did what the Lord had told him to do. He went to the Kerwith Valley. It was east of the Jordan River. He stayed there. The ravens brought him bread and meat in the morning. They also brought him bread and meat in the evening. He drank water from the brook. Some time later the brook dried up. It hadn't rained in the land for quite a while." – *1 Kings 17:2-7*

Elijah followed God's directions and was provided for in the valley. God provided ravens to feed him bread and meat every morning and night. God also provided running water from a brook in the middle of a drought. In this part of the story Elijah's supply of water dried up. He was obedient to follow God and he left when God told him it was time to go.

Common Stressors for Teens:

Really in no certain order, published by Maria Magher, eHow Contributor, July 26, 2014

1.	School and Grades	6.	Popularity
2.	Family Issues (divorce)	7.	Romantic Relationships
3.	Body Image	8.	Cyber Bullying
4.	Finances	9.	Changes
5.	Criticism	10.	Siblings

Activity 5: What are your top 10?

1. _____   6. _____

2. _____   7. _____

3. _____   8. _____

4. _____   9. _____

5. _____   10. _____

Activity 6:

➡ Think about what you need to stop doing in your life. Think about a habit, pattern, or behavior that is causing you problems, or getting you into trouble. Is it time for that to end in your life?

I want to stop ...

I am going to walk away and this is how ...

➡ Use the space below to draw or write about what you want to stop. Then use the next page to write a prayer asking God to help you stop.

Prayer

Dear God,

Please help me ...

Thank you, Amen.

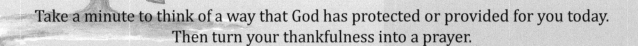

Take a minute to think of a way that God has protected or provided for you today.
Then turn your thankfulness into a prayer.

Another Story of Provision

"A message came to Elijah from the Lord. He said, "Go right away to Zarephath in the territory of Sidon. Stay there. I have commanded a widow in that place to supply you with food."

So Elijah went to Zarephath. He came to the town gate. A widow was there gathering sticks. He called out to her. He asked, "Would you bring me a little water in a jar? I need a drink."

She went to get the water. Then he called out to her, "Please bring me a piece of bread too."

"I don't have any bread," she replied. "And that's just as sure as the Lord your God is alive. All I have is a small amount of flour in a jar and a little olive oil in a jug. I'm gathering a few sticks to take home. I'll make one last meal for myself and my son. We'll eat it. After that, we'll die."

Elijah said to her, "Don't be afraid. Go home. Do what you have said. But first make a little bread for me. Make it out of what you have. Bring it to me. Then make some for yourself and your son.

Elijah said to her, "Don't be afraid."

"The Lord is the God of Israel. He says, 'The jar of flour will not be used up. The jug will always have oil in it. You will have flour and oil until the day the Lord sends rain on the land.'"

She went away and did what Elijah had told her to do. So Elijah had food every day. There was also food for the woman and her family. The jar of flour wasn't used up. The jug always had oil in it. That's what the Lord had said would happen. He had spoken that message through Elijah." – *1 Kings 17:8-16*

Activity 7: What is another word for fear?

Take a few moments to look at the feeling dolls on page 5. Choose a word to describe what fear looks like for you.

Activity 8:

 Fill in this bird with everything that God has given you. List people, possessions, experiences, friends, school, sports and more.

What Have I Done Wrong?

Some time later the son of the woman who owned the house became sick. He got worse and worse. Finally he stopped breathing. The woman said to Elijah, "You are a man of God. What do you have against me? Did you come to bring my sin out into the open? Did you come to kill my son?"

"Give me your son," Elijah replied. He took him from her arms. He carried him to the upstairs room where he was staying. He put him down on his bed. Then Elijah cried out to the Lord. He said, "Lord my God, I'm staying with this widow. Have you brought pain and sorrow to her? Have you caused her son to die?" Then he lay down on the boy three times. He cried out to the Lord. He said, "Lord my God, give this boy's life back to him!"

"Did you come to bring my sin out into the open? Did you come to kill my son?"

The Lord answered Elijah's prayer. He gave the boy's life back to him. So the boy lived. Elijah picked up the boy. He carried him down from the upstairs room into the house. He gave him to his mother. He said, "Look! Your son is alive!"

Then the woman said to Elijah, "Now I know that you are a man of God. I know that the message you have brought from the Lord is true." – *1 Kings 17:17-24*

In this story the widow was devastated when her son died. She was so upset that she asked the question: What did I do wrong to make this happen? It is sometimes difficult to understand why God would let something bad happen. It is very important for us to stop and understand that God created you, just like he created Elijah, the widow and her son. God loves you.

Bad things happen in the world because when Adam and Eve ate of the forbidden fruit, sin, darkness and shame entered into the world.

Before Adam and Eve ate the forbidden fruit they were walking around the garden. They were naked and not ashamed. They would spend the "days" talking with God.

After they ate the fruit they immediately ran to hide and then covered up their naked bodies. Shame is not from God. Shame entered the world with sin from Satan.

Shame often shows itself in the question, "What did I do wrong?" Although there are times when we are to blame and there are natural consequences for breaking God's law, when we ask for forgiveness God does not see our sin anymore.

Activity 9:

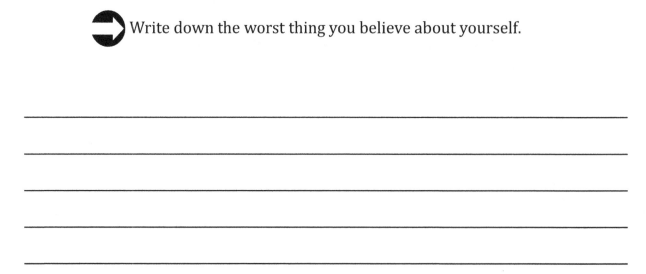 Write down the worst thing you believe about yourself.

_____

_____

_____

_____

Activity 10:

➡ Using colors, images and words... draw the things you believe about yourself in the first doll, then use the second doll to illustrate what God says about you.

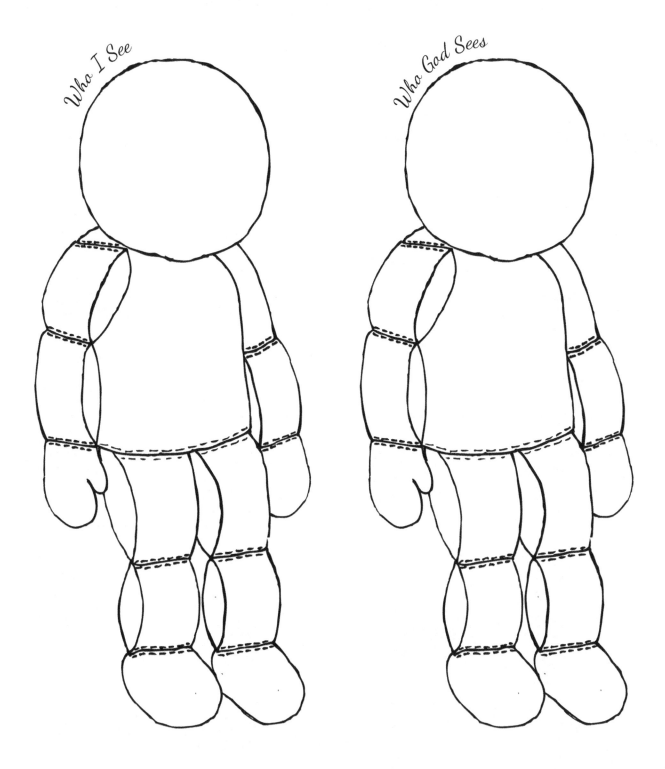

Who I See

Who God Sees

Prayer

"_____ was fearfully and wonderfully made,
your name here

created in the image of God." – *Psalm 139:14, Genesis 1:27 NASB*

➡ Add a few verses to fill in with your name.

_____

_____

_____

_____

_____

_____

_____

_____

_____

Take a minute to think of a way that God has protected or provided for you today.
Then turn your thankfulness into a prayer.

How to Find a Good Friend
How to Be a Good Friend

"It was now three years since it had rained. A message came to Elijah from the Lord. He said, "Go. Speak to Ahab. Then I will send rain on the land.""

So Elijah went to speak to Ahab.

There wasn't enough food in Samaria. The people there were very hungry. Ahab had sent for Obadiah. He was in charge of Ahab's palace. Obadiah had great respect for the Lord.

Ahab's wife Jezebel had been killing off the Lord's prophets. So Obadiah had hidden 100 prophets in two caves. He had put 50 in each cave. He had supplied them with food and water.

Ahab had said to Obadiah, "Go through the land. Go to all of the springs of water and to the valleys. Maybe we can find some grass there. It will keep the horses and mules alive. Then we won't have to kill any of our animals." So they decided where each of them would look. Ahab went in one direction. Obadiah went in another.

As Obadiah was walking along, Elijah met him. Obadiah recognized him. He bowed down to the ground. He said, "My master Elijah! Is it really you?"

"Yes," he replied. "Go and tell your master Ahab, 'Elijah is here.'"

"What have I done wrong?" asked Obadiah. "Why are you handing me over to Ahab to be put to death?

"My master has sent people to look for you everywhere. There isn't a nation or kingdom where he hasn't sent someone to look for you. Suppose a nation or kingdom would claim you weren't there. Then Ahab would make them take an oath and say they couldn't find you. And that's just as sure as the Lord your God is alive.

"What have I done wrong?" asked Obadiah

"But now you are telling me to go to my master. You want me to say, 'Elijah is here.' But the Spirit of the Lord might carry you away when I leave you. Then I won't know where you are. If I go and tell Ahab and he doesn't find you, he'll kill me.

"But I've worshiped the Lord ever since I was young. My master, haven't you heard what I did? Jezebel was killing the Lord's prophets. But I hid 100 of them in two caves.

I put 50 in each cave. I supplied them with food and water. And now you are telling me to go to my master Ahab. You want me to say to him, 'Elijah is here.' He'll kill me!"

Elijah said, "I serve the Lord who rules over all. You can be sure that he lives. And you can be just as sure that I will speak to Ahab today." – *1 Kings 18:1-15*

When Elijah met Obadiah, at first Obadiah was very excited to see him. He was encouraged to meet someone so famous. But after Elijah asked him to go tell King Ahab he was coming… Obadiah wasn't so happy. In fact, he said the same thing the widow did when her son died: "What have I done wrong?" Obadiah questioned how he had made a mistake that God would ask him to do something so hard.

Have you ever known in your heart you should be a good friend when someone is being mistreated or bullied but you knew it would be hard? Or maybe your "so called friends" are not treating you well. God teaches us to make wise decisions. If your friends or the people you are hanging out with are making poor decisions (doing wrong things, treating others badly, or treating you with disrespect) stop hanging out with them.

Activity 11:

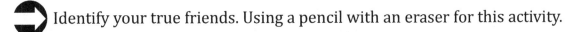 Identify your true friends. Using a pencil with an eraser for this activity.

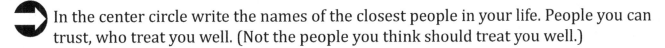 In the center circle write the names of the closest people in your life. People you can trust, who treat you well. (Not the people you think should treat you well.)

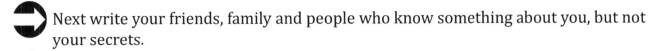 Next write your friends, family and people who know something about you, but not your secrets.

➡ The outside circle is for people you know as acquaintances, like the school secretary, the clerk at your favorite store, or your parents' or siblings' friends.

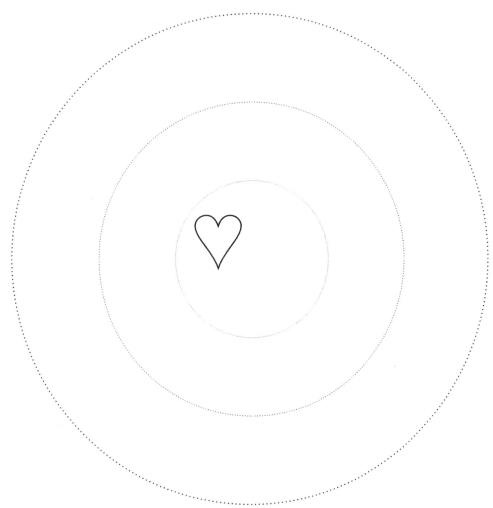

➡ Now look at all the names on your circles. Is there anyone is your center circle who is treating you poorly? Is there anyone in one of your outer circles that treats you with kindness and respect? Consider moving the people who treat you well closer to your heart.

God's word says:

"Do not throw your pearls before swine." – *Matthew 7:6 NASB*

This means, don't throw your precious jewelry into a pig pen. Friends treat each other with care and respect. It is important to choose your friends wisely.

Activity 12: Friendship.

What makes you a good friend?

_____

_____

_____

_____

What are the things you look for in a friend?

_____

_____

_____

_____

Take a minute to think of a way that God has protected or provided for you today.
Then turn your thankfulness into a prayer.

The Big Showdown

Obadiah went back to Ahab. He told Ahab that Elijah wanted to see him. So Ahab went to where Elijah was. When he saw Elijah, he said to him, "Is that you? You are always stirring up trouble in Israel."

"I haven't made trouble for Israel," Elijah replied. "But you and your father's family have. You have turned away from the Lord's commands. You have followed the gods that are named after Baal.

"Now send for people from all over Israel. Tell them to meet me on Mount Carmel. And bring the 450 prophets of the god Baal. Also bring the 400 prophets of the goddess Asherah. All of them eat at Jezebel's table."

So Ahab sent that message all through Israel. He gathered the prophets together on Mount Carmel.

Elijah went there and stood in front of the people. He said, "How long will it take you to make up your minds? If the Lord is the one and only God, follow him. But if Baal is the one and only God, follow him."

The people didn't say anything.

"Then you pray to your god. And I'll pray to the LORD. The god who answers is the one and only God."

Then Elijah said to them, "I'm the only one of the Lord's prophets left. But Baal has 450 prophets. Get two bulls for us. Let Baal's prophets choose one for themselves. Let them cut it into pieces. Then let them put it on the wood. But don't let them set fire to it. I'll prepare the other bull. I'll put it on the wood. But I won't set fire to it. Then you pray to your god. And I'll pray to the Lord. The god who answers by sending fire down is the one and only God."

Then all of the people said, "What you are saying is good."

Elijah spoke to the prophets of Baal. He said, "Choose one of the bulls. There are many of you. So prepare your bull first. Pray to your god. But don't light the fire."

So they prepared the bull they had been given.

They prayed to Baal from morning until noon. "Baal! Answer us!" they shouted. But there wasn't any reply. No one answered. Then they danced around the altar they had made.

At noon Elijah began to tease them. "Shout louder!" he said. "I'm sure Baal is a god! Perhaps he has too much to think about. Or maybe he has gone to the toilet. Or perhaps he's away on a trip. Maybe he's sleeping. You might have to wake him up."

So they shouted louder. [The prophets of Baal] cut themselves with swords and spears until their blood flowed. That's what they usually did when things really looked hopeless. It was now past noon. The prophets of Baal continued to [call out] with all their might. They did it until the time came to offer the evening sacrifice. But there wasn't any reply. No one answered. No one paid any attention.

Then Elijah said to all of the people, "Come here to me." So they went to him. He rebuilt the altar of the Lord. It had been destroyed. Elijah got 12 stones. There was one for each tribe in the family line of Jacob. The Lord's message had come to Jacob. It had said, "Your name will be Israel." Elijah used the stones to build an altar in honor of the Lord. He dug a ditch around it. The ditch was large enough to hold 13 quarts of seeds. He arranged the wood for the fire. He cut the bull into pieces. He placed the pieces on the wood.

Then he said to some of the people, "Fill four large jars with water. Pour it on the offering and the wood." So they did.

"Do it again," he said. So they did it again.

"Do it a third time," he ordered. And they did it the third time. The water ran down around the altar. It even filled the ditch.

"Answer me. LORD, answer me. Then these people will know that you are the one and only God.

When it was time to offer the evening sacrifice, the prophet Elijah stepped forward. He prayed, "Lord, you are the God of Abraham, Isaac and Israel. Today let everyone know that you are God in Israel. Let them know I'm your servant. Let them know I've done all of these things because you commanded me to. Answer me. Lord, answer me. Then these people will know that you are the one and only God. They'll know that you are turning their hearts back to you again."

The fire of the Lord came down. It burned up the sacrifice. It burned up the wood and the stones and the soil. It even licked up the water in the ditch.

All of the people saw it. Then they fell down flat with their faces toward the ground. They cried out, "The Lord is the one and only God! The Lord is the one and only God!" – *1 Kings 18:16-39*

Activity 13: What are your idols?

Idols are more than little Buddha statues. They are anything we put faith in over God. What are the things, people, or experiences that you put before God? (sports, money, a girlfriend or boyfriend)

Make a list of the things you worship or put before God.

_____

_____

_____

_____

Prayer

Dear God,

Please help me ...

Thank you, Amen.

Take a minute to think of a way that God has protected or provided for you today.
Then turn your thankfulness into a prayer.

But I'm Scared

Ahab told Jezebel everything Elijah had done. He told her how Elijah had killed all of the prophets with his sword.

So Jezebel sent a message to Elijah. She said, "You can be sure that I will kill you, just as I killed the other prophets. I'll do it by this time tomorrow. If I don't, may the gods punish me greatly."

Elijah was afraid. So he ran for his life. He came to Beersheba in Judah. He left his servant there.

Then he traveled for one day into the desert. He came to a small tree. He sat down under it. He prayed that he would die. "Lord, I've had enough," he said. "Take my life. I'm no better than my people of long ago." Then he lay down under the tree. And he fell asleep." – *1 Kings 19:1-5*

"Take my life. I am no better than my people of long ago."

Elijah had seen God do one miracle after another. He had seen God "show up." And when faced with the threat of death, he ran away... he started off angry with God and later ended up exhausted and feeling hopeless. He was so sad he wished to be dead.

You might wonder what this has to do with you. Have you ever done the right thing, made really good decisions and choices and then been accused of something you didn't do? Maybe you even received a consequence or punishment that wasn't fair.

Sometimes when you begin to follow God's way: the Ten Commandments and Jesus way: "to love others more than ourselves" you actually find that your life is harder. This is what happened to Elijah. He had obeyed God and still ended up having Queen Jezebel threaten his life.

Activity 14: Scared

➡ Using colors, images and words...
draw what it feels like when you are scared.

Activity 15:

What scares you?

What is your biggest fear?

When you are scared what do you idolize, worship, or put before God?

Who will you share your fear with? _____
a trusted adult, mentor, parent
or other family member

What makes you feel safe?

How do you keep yourself feeling safe?

➡ Use the next page to write a prayer asking God to help you release your fear.

Prayer

Dear God,

Please help me ...

Thank you, Amen.

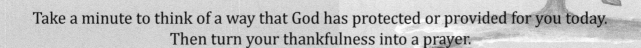

Take a minute to think of a way that God has protected or provided for you today.
Then turn your thankfulness into a prayer.

Activity 16: Sad

Using colors, images and words...
draw a picture of what you look like when you feel sad.

Activity 17: Joy

➡ Using colors, images and words...
draw a picture of what you look like when you feel glad (happy).

Activity 18: Mad

Using colors, images and words...
draw a picture of what you look like when you feel angry.

Activity 19:

Make a copy of this page and hang it in your bedroom or on your mirror. Every day for a month fill in how you are feeling that day.

For Instance

What's a Broom Tree Anyway?

Suddenly an angel touched him. The angel said, "Get up and eat." Elijah looked around. Near his head he saw a flat cake of bread. It had been baked over hot coals. A jar of water was also there. So Elijah ate and drank. Then he lay down again.

The angel of the Lord came to him a second time. He touched him and said, "Get up and eat. Your journey will be long and hard."

So he got up. He ate and drank. The food gave him new strength. He traveled for 40 days and 40 nights. He kept going until he arrived at Mount Horeb. It was the mountain of God. There he went into a cave and spent the night.
– *1 Kings 19:5-9*

"He ate and drank. The food gave him new strength."

A broom tree is a place you go to or an activity you do which brings enjoyment, relaxation or rest.

35

Activity 20: Broom Tree

➡ Using colors and words write a minimum of five things you like to do when you are not at school, doing homework or chores.

1. _____

2. _____

3. _____

4. _____

5. _____

When do you feel most relaxed?

What activities do you enjoy?

When is the last time you have done one of these activities?

What is an activity you have always wanted to try?

If it has been longer than two weeks since you have done one of these fun, relaxing activities please share this activity with a trusted adult, mentor, parent, or other family member. Make a plan to do a broom tree activity.

Activity 21:

 Fill in your tree with activities that bring you relaxation, refreshment and rest.

I Don't Know What God Sounds Like!
The Lord Appears to Elijah

"A message came to Elijah from the Lord. He said, "Elijah, what are you doing here?"

He replied, "Lord God who rules over all, I've been very committed to you. The people of Israel have turned their backs on your covenant. They have torn down your altars. They've put your prophets to death with their swords. I'm the only one left. And they are trying to kill me."

The Lord said, "Go out. Stand on the mountain in front of me. I am going to pass by."

As the Lord approached, a very powerful wind tore the mountains apart. It broke up the rocks. But the Lord wasn't in the wind.

After the wind there was an earthquake. But the Lord wasn't in the earthquake.

After the earthquake a fire came. But the Lord wasn't in the fire.

And after the fire there was only a gentle whisper. When Elijah heard it, he pulled his coat over his face. He went out and stood at the entrance to the cave. – *1 Kings 19:9-13*

Activity 22:

Lectio Divina (Big word which means ... Holy Reading)

➲ *1* **Read**
Read 1 Kings 19:9-13. Write down the words and images that stand out. Draw a picture.

➲ *2* **Meditate**
Read 1 Kings 19:9-13 a second time. Underline what stands out.

➲ *3* **Pray**
Read 1 Kings 19:9-13 a third time. Pick one word that stands out.

➲ *4* **Contemplate**
Quietly rest in the presence of God.

Activity 23:

➤ Get a Bible, a journal, and a devotion book (Living the Elijah Project).

➤ Begin to spend 5 to 10 minutes with God every day.

➤ **Every day write down:**

what you feel

how God is providing for you

how God is protecting you

then pray.

This will help you hear from God.

Imagine Your Story

Elijah's story did not end at verse 13 of *1 Kings 19*.
Your story doesn't end at the end of this workbook.

Activity 24:

➡ Use the comic strip form (below) to write or draw about your future, imagining your goals and accomplishments. What is your dream for your future? Dream!

#1

#2

#3

#4

Prayer

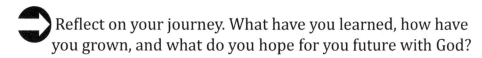 Reflect on your journey. What have you learned, how have you grown, and what do you hope for you future with God?

Dear God,

Please help me ...

Thank you, Amen.

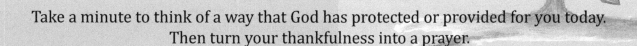

Take a minute to think of a way that God has protected or provided for you today.
Then turn your thankfulness into a prayer.

... The journey continues

We invite you to learn more about The Elijah Project at
andreapolnaszek.com

For information about having the author speak
at your school or church please contact:

Andrea M. Polnaszek, LCSW
apolnaszek@mac.com
715-379-0858

Made in United States
North Haven, CT
19 June 2022

20414317R00030